# CLAS
# WEST COUNTRY
# GHOST STORIES

COMPILED BY PAUL WHITE

# TOR MARK

Published by Tor Mark Ltd,
United Downs Industrial Estate,
Redruth, Cornwall TR16 5HY

www.tormark.co.uk

First published 1996, reprinted 2009
This edition 2023

ISBN 9780 85025 491 4

Text: © Tor Mark Ltd, compiled by Paul White
Images: © Adobe 2023, © Shutterstock 2023

Printed and bound in the UK

 Printed on FSC Mix

# CONTENTS

# INTRODUCTION

The West Country (Cornwall, Devon, Dorset and Somerset) has more ghosts than any other region of England, and this book contains a selection of the most intriguing tales of ghosts and apparitions from the area.

These stories have come from many sources, most notably Mrs Bray, Mrs Crowe, John Ingram, Rev Sabine Baring-Gould, Lord Halifax, Augustus Hare, TM Jarvis, Arthur Norway and Henry Spicer. They have been selected for readability rather than psychical authenticity, and you certainly do not need to believe in ghosts in order to enjoy them.

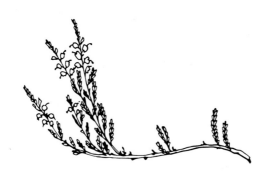

# THE HAUNTED NUNNERY

The following narration, apparently by Richard Bovet, was published in 1823, in an early and influential classic of ghost literature, *Accredited Ghost Stories* by TM Jarvis.

About the year 1667 I was staying with some persons of honour in the house of a nobleman in the west country which had formerly been a nunnery. I must confess I had often heard the servants and others that inhabited or lodged there speak much of the noises, stirs and apparitions that frequently disturbed the house, but had at that time no apprehensions of it; for, the house being full of strangers, the nobleman's steward Mr C- lay with me in a fine wainscot room, called My Lady's Chamber. We went to our lodging pretty early and having a good fire in the room we spent some time in reading, in which he much delighted; then, having got into bed and put out the candles, we observed the room to be very light by brightness of the moon, so that a wager was laid between us that it was possible to read written hand by that light upon the bed where we lay.

We had scarce made an end of discoursing on that affair, when I saw (my face being toward the door, which was locked) entering into the room five appearances of very fine and lovely women; they were of excellent stature, and their dresses seemed very fine, their faces all but covered with their light veils and whose skirts trailed largely upon the floor. They entered in a file, one after the other, and in that posture walked around the room, till the foremost came and stood by that side of the bed on which I lay (with my left arm over the side of the bed for my head rested on that arm and I determined not to alter the posture in which I was); she struck me upon that hand with a blow that felt very soft, but I did never remember whether it were cold or hot. I demanded in the name of the blessed Trinity what business they had there but received no answer.

Then I spoke to Mr C- 'Sir, do you see what fair guests we have, come to visit us?' before which they all disappeared. I found him in some kind of agony and was forced to grasp him on the breast with my right hand (which was next him under the bedclothes) before I could obtain speech of him. Then he told me he had seen the fair guests I spoke of and had heard me speak to them; but withal said that he was not able to speak sooner unto me, being extremely frighted at the sight of a dreadful monster, which, assuming a shape betwixt that of a lion and a bear, attempted to come upon the bed's foot. I told him I thanked God nothing so frightful had presented itself to me but I hoped (through His assistance) not to dread the ambages of hell. It was a long time before I could compose him to speak and though he had had many disturbances in his own room, and understood of others in the house, yet he acknowledged he had never been so terrified during many years abode there.

The next day, at dinner, he showed to many persons of principal quality the mark that had been occasioned on his breast by the gripe I was forced to give him to get him to speak, and related all the passages very exactly after which he protested never to lie more in that room upon which I set up a resolution to lodge in it again, not knowing but something of the reason of those troubles might by that means be imparted to me.

The next night therefore, I ordered a bible and another book to be laid in the room, and resolved to spend my time by the fire, in reading and contemplation, till I found myself inclined to sleep; and accordingly, having taken leave of the family at the usual hour, I addressed myself to what I proposed, not going to bed till past one in the morning. A little after I was got into bed I heard someone walk about the room, like a woman in a tabby gown trailing about the room; it made a mighty rustling noise but I could see nothing, though it was near as light as the night before. It passed by the foot of the bed, and a little opened the curtain, and thence went to a closet room on that side, through which it found admittance, although it was close locked. There it seemed to groan, and draw a great chair with its foot, in which it seemed to sit and turn over the leaves of a large folio, which, you know, make a loud clattering noise. It continued in that posture, sometimes groaning, sometimes dragging the chair and clattering the book, till it was near day. Afterwards I lodged several times in this room, but never met with molestation.

This I can attest to be a true account of what passed in that room the two described nights and although Mr C- be lately dead, who was a very ingenious man, and affirmed the first part unto many with whom he was conversant, it remains that I appeal to the knowledge of those who have been inhabitants or lodgers in the said house for what remains to justify the credibility of the rest.

# MURDER WILL OUT

I n the first half of the eighteenth century the well-known family of Harris from Heyne were residing at their ancient seat in the county of Devon, not far from the borders of Cornwall. The family was wealthy and their estates extended far and wide round the mansion. The head of the family at that time held a situation in the court of George II, which obliged him to reside in London during a part of the year.

When the time of his attendance at court arrived, Mr Harris was accustomed to move the greater part of his establishment to London, leaving behind a few servants only, under the charge of Richard Morris, who had been long in the family as head butler.

In the year 1730, when Mr Harris was in London, he received a letter from his confidential servant, informing him that the house had been broken into at night, and that a lad who had lately been taken into service had mysteriously disappeared. Mr Harris immediately left London for his seat in Devonshire, and on his arrival was told that no alarm had been given on the night of the robbery until the morning, when a window opening on the lawn was discovered to have been broken through, and footstep marks discovered outside. Morris, the butler was found in the plate-room, half-dressed, tied to a table, and with a gag in his mouth. His own account of the robbery was that having been roused by some noise in the middle of the night, he had got up and gone down to the plate-room, the door of which had been previously forced, that he was there seized, gagged and bound before he could escape, or even call for help; and that there were five or six men altogether, none of whom he recognised, except the lad lately taken into service, who had disappeared since that night.

In those days there were no detectives or rural police. A week had elapsed before Mr Harris could reach his home. In the meanwhile, the village constables had attempted to trace out the robbers, but without success. No clue to the missing plate or the thieves could be discovered. After making a careful and strict search of the premises, Mr Harris returned to his court duties in London, giving up all hope of finding either his lost property or the criminals.

Some six months passed before Mr Harris again visited his country seat, where he was received by Morris, and found everything in its usual state, nothing more having been ascertained about the robbery. Tired with his long journey from town, Mr Harris retired early to bed, and soon fell into a sound sleep. In the middle of the night he suddenly awoke - as he himself was always wont to declare on relating the incident, he was in an instant wide awake, how or why he never could explain - and he saw by the light of a small lamp burning in his room the lad who had disappeared on the night when the plate was stolen, standing at the foot of the bed. Mr Harris asked what he wanted at that time of night; the boy beckoned to him but made no reply. Again, he asked him for what purpose he had come, and again the boy beckoned to him and pointed to the door.

Mr Harris was as devoid of fear as any man  so he rose from his bed, partly dressed himself, took his sword under his arm, and then followed the lad, still beckoning and pointing with his arm out of the room. His own subsequent statement of his feelings was that he was in doubt as to whether the lad was alive or an apparition, that he felt no fear, but only a strong desire and determination to see the matter to an end. The two went down the staircase and through a side door, which Mr Harris remembers to have been to his astonishment unlocked, and entered the park.

The lad led the way for about a hundred yards towards a very large oak, the trunk of which was surrounded and almost hidden by low shrubs and bushes, which had been allowed to grow wild from time immemorial. Here the lad stopped, pointed to the ground with his forefinger, and then seemed to pass towards the other side of the tree. It was not a dark night, and when Mr Harris followed, as he immediately did, the lad had vanished from his sight. It seemed useless to search for him, and after a little while Mr Harris returned to the house, fastened the door as he let himself in, and went to his room for the remainder of the night.

Before the dawn he had resolved on his course of action, and, having made his arrangements, he first had the butler, Richard Morris, taken into custody. He then set workmen to dig round the oak tree, who after a short search came upon the body of the lad, buried in his clothes, scarcely a foot below the surface. It was evident that his death was occasioned by strangulation, as the cord was still tightly fastened about his neck.

The butler, after attempting at first to deny having had any hand in the business, soon made a confession of the whole affair. He had two accomplices to help him in the robbery, who had carried off the stolen plate to Plymouth, but being interrupted by the lad whilst removing it, they had murdered him, and buried his body under the tree. They then proceeded to tie and gag the butler, as he was found in the pantry. The murderers were never traced, and so escaped the penalty of their crime; but Morris the butler was tried at the ensuing Exeter assizes, pleaded guilty and was executed.

The details given above were mentioned at the trial of Richard Morris as explaining the cause of his being suspected and of his subsequent arrest. Mr Harris always avowed most solemnly the reality of the apparition, and that he had actually gone out of the house in the dead of night, and accompanied the spirit of the murdered lad to the very spot where he had been buried. Though all who are disbelievers in supernatural appearances will readily attribute it to the effect of a dream, this plausible theory will not account for the fact of the place where the lad was buried having been so quickly found.

## THE WADEBRIDGE MURDER

On the evening of the 8th of February 1840, Mr Nevell Norway, a Cornish gentleman, was cruelly murdered by two brothers, of the name of Lightfoot, on his way from Bodmin to Wadebridge, the place of his residence. At that time, his brother, Mr Edmund Norway, was in the command of a merchant vessel, the Orient, on her voyage from Manilla to Cadiz; and the following is his own account of a dream which he had on the night when his brother was murdered:

About 7.30pm, the island of St Helena N.N.W., distant about seven miles shortened sail and rounded to with the ship's head to the eastward; at eight, set the watch and went below; wrote a letter to my brother, Nevell. About twenty minutes or a quarter before ten o'clock, went to bed; fell asleep and dreamt I saw two men attack my brother and murder him. One caught the horse by the

bridle, and snapped a pistol twice, but I heard no report; he then struck him a blow, and he fell off the horse. They struck him several blows and dragged him by the shoulders across the road and left him. In my dream, there was a house on the left hand side of the road. At four o'clock I was called and went on deck to take charge of the ship. I told the second officer, Mr Henry Wren, that I had had a dreadful dream - namely that my brother Nevell was murdered by two men on the road from St Columb to Wadebridge, but that I felt sure that it could not be there, as the house there would be on the right-hand side of the road; so that it must have been somewhere else. He replied, 'Don't think anything about it; you west-country people are so superstitious. You will make yourself miserable for the remainder of the voyage.' He then left the general orders and went below. It was one continued dream from the time I fell asleep until I was called at four o'clock in the morning.

Edmund Norway
Chief Officer, Ship Orient

The confession of William Lightfoot, one of the assassins who really did murder Nevell Norway, and who was executed, together with his brother, for the crime, at Bodmin on the 13th April 1840, is as follows:

'I went to Bodmin last Saturday week, the 8th February, and in returning I met my brother at the top of Dummer Hill. It was dim like. We came on the turnpike road all the way till we came to the house near the spot where the murder was committed. We did not go into the house, but hid ourselves in a field. My brother knocked Mr Norway down; he snapped a pistol at him twice and it did not go off. He then knocked him down with the pistol. I was there along with him. Mr Norway was struck while on horseback. It was on the turnpike road between Pencarron Mill and the directing post towards Wadebridge. I cannot say at what time of the night it was. We left the body in the water, on the left side of the road coming to Wadebridge. We took some money in a purse, but I did not know how much. My brother drew the body across the road to the water.'

The evidence of various witnesses called at the trial of the assassins proved that the murder must have been committed between ten and eleven at night.

Dr Carlyon, in concluding his account of the dream in Early Years and Late Reflections, remarks, 'It will be seen that Mr Edmund Norway, in relating his dream to his shipmate, observed that the murder could not have been committed on the St Columb road because the house, in going thence to Wadebridge, is on the right hand, whereas the house was, in his dream, on the left.

'Now this circumstance, however apparently trivial, tends somewhat to enhance the interest of the dream, without in the least impugning its fidelity; for such fissures are characteristic of these sensorial impressions, which are altogether involuntary, and bear a much nearer relation to the productions of the daguerreotype than to those of the portrait-painter, whose lines are at his command.'

## STEER NOR'WEST

Torquay, before it was 'discovered' and turned into a fashionable winter residence and watering place, was a quiet fishing village, consisting of a few cottages, under richly wooded hills. In one of those cottages, at the close of the eighteenth century, lived a sailor named Robert Bruce.

When he reached the age of thirty he became first mate of a ship sailing between Liverpool and St John, New Brunswick. On one of these periodical voyages westwards, after having been at sea six weeks, and being near the Banks of Newfoundland, the captain and mate, after having taken an observation, went below into the cabin to calculate their day's work.

The mate, Robert Bruce, absorbed in his reckonings, which did not answer his expectations, had not noticed that the captain had risen and left the cabin as soon as he had completed his calculations. Without raising his head, he called out, 'I say, cap'n, I make the latitude and longitude to be so-and-so. Not what it ought to be. What is your reckoning?'

As he received no reply, he repeated the question, and glancing over his shoulder and seeing, as he supposed, the captain figuring on his slate, he asked a third time, and again without eliciting a reply. Surprised and vexed, he stood up, and to his inexpressible astonishment, saw that the seated man, engaged on the slate, was not the captain, but an entire stranger. He noted his features and his garments, both wholly different from those of his superior officer. At the same moment the stranger raised his head and looked him full in the eyes. The face was that of a

man he had never seen before in his life. Much disturbed, he slipped up the ladder, and seeing the captain, went to him, and in an agitated voice told him there was a total stranger in the cabin, at the captain's desk, engaged in writing.

'A stranger!' exclaimed the captain. 'Impossible! You must have been dreaming. The steward or second mate may have gone down for aught I know.'
'No, sir; it was neither. I saw the man occupying your armchair. He looked me full in the face, and I saw him as plainly as I see you now.'
'Impossible!' said the captain. 'Do you know who he is?'
'Never saw the man in my life before - an utter stranger.'
'You must have gone daft, Mr Bruce. Why, we have been six weeks at sea, and you know every man Jack who is on board.
"I know that, sir; but a stranger is there, I assure you.'
'Go down again, Mr Bruce, and ask his name.'
The mate hesitated. 'I'm not a superstitious man,' said he, 'but hang it, I don't relish the idea of facing him again alone.'

'Well, well,' said the captain, laughing, 'I don't mind accompanying you. This is not like you, Bruce, not like you at all - you're not in liquor. It's a mere delusion.'

The captain descended the stairs accompanied by the mate; and sure enough, the cabin was empty.

'There you are, convicted of dreaming,' said the former. 'Did I not tell you as much?'

'I can't say how it was, sir,' replied Bruce, 'but I could take my oath on the Gospels that I saw a man writing on your slate.'

'If he wrote, there must be something to show for it,' said the captain, as he took up the slate, and at once exclaimed, 'Why, - good God! There is something here. Is this your fist, Mr Bruce?' The mate examined the slate, and there in plain legible characters stood the words 'Steer to the Nor'west.'

'You have been playing tricks,' said the captain impatiently.

'On my word as a man and a sailor, sir,' replied Bruce, 'I know no more about this matter than just what I told you.'

The captain mused, seated himself, and handing over the slate to the mate, said, 'You write on the back of this slate, Steer to the Nor'west.'

Bruce did as required, and the captain narrowly compared the two writings; they differed entirely.

'Send down the second mate,' he ordered.

Bruce did as required. On his entering the cabin, the captain bade him write the same words, and he did so. The handwriting was again different. Next the steward was sent for, as also every one of the crew who could write, and the result was the same. At length the captain said, 'There must be a stowaway. Have the ship searched. Pipe all hands on deck.' Every corner of the vessel was explored, but all in vain. The captain was more perplexed than ever. Summoning the mate to attend him in the cabin, and holding the slate before him, he asked Bruce what he considered this might mean.

'That is more than I can say, sir,' replied Bruce. 'I saw the man write, and there you see the writing. There must be something in it we don't understand.'

'Well,' said the captain, 'it does look like it. We have the wind fine, and I have a good mind to keep her away and see what comes of it all.'

'If I were in your place, sir, that is what I would do. It is only a few hours lost, at the worst.'

'It shall be so. Go and give the course, Nor'west, and Mr Bruce, have a good look-out aloft; and let it be a hand you can depend upon.'

The mate gave the required orders, and about 3pm he reported an iceberg nearly ahead, and shortly after, that he observed a vessel close to it. As they approached, by aid of his telescope, the captain discerned a dismantled ship, apparently wedged and frozen into the ice, and he was able to distinguish a good many human beings on it. Shortly after, he hove to and sent out boats to the relief of the sufferers.

The vessel proved to be one from Quebec, bound to Liverpool, with passengers on board. She had become entangled in the ice, and finally frozen fast, and had been in this condition for several weeks. She was stove in, her decks swept, and was, in fact, a mere wreck. All her provisions, and almost all her water, had been consumed, and crew and passengers had despaired of being saved, and looked out for a watery grave. Their gratitude for this unexpected deliverance was proportionately great.

As one of the men, who had been brought away in the third boat that had reached the wreck, was ascending the ship's side, the mate, catching a glimpse of his face, started back in astonishment. He recognised the identical face that he had seen in the cabin, three or four hours before, looking up at him from the captain's desk. When the man stood on the deck, Bruce examined him closely. Not only was the face the same, but in person and dress he corresponded exactly with his vision.

As soon as the exhausted crew and passengers had been fed and cared for, and the bark was on her course again, the mate called the captain aside, and said, 'That was no ghost, sir, that I saw this morning. The man is here, alive, and on board our boat.'

'What do you mean?'
'Sir,' said Bruce, very gravely, 'one of the passengers we have just saved is the very same person that I saw writing on your slate at noon. I would swear to the identity in any court of justice.'

'This is becoming more strange and inexplicable every minute,' said the captain. 'Let us go and have a look at the man.'

They found him in conversation with the captain of the derelict vessel when both expressed their warmest gratitude for their deliverance from a terrible fate, either starvation and exposure, or drowning should the iceberg have collapsed.

The captain replied that he had done no more than was his duty, and that he was quite sure that they would have done the same for him under similar circumstances; and then he requested both to step down with him into his cabin.

When that was done, turning to the passenger he said, 'Will you excuse the liberty I am taking with you, if I desire you to write a few words on the slate?'
'Certainly I will do so,' said the passenger. 'What shall I write?'
'Nothing more than this, Steer to the Nor'west.'

The passenger looked amazed and puzzled; however, he held out his hand for the slate. This the captain extended to him, with that side uppermost on which Bruce and the crew had written, which writing he had effaced with a sponge. The man wrote the required words. The captain took back the slate and, stepping aside while the passenger was not observing, turned the slate over, and presented it to him, with the side uppermost on which was the mysterious inscription.

Tendering the slate again to him, he said: 'You are ready to swear, sir, that this is your handwriting?'
'Of course it is; you saw me write.'
'Look at it attentively, and make sure it is the same.'
'I have no doubt about it. I make my *s* in the midst of a sentence in the old-fashioned way, long. And there it is, attached to the *t* at steer and west.'
'And this also?' asked the captain, turning the slate over.

The passenger looked first at one writing, then at the other, quite confounded.

'I don't understand what this can mean,' said he; 'I wrote the words once only. Who wrote the other?'
'That, sir, is more than I can say. My mate informs me that you wrote it, sitting at my desk at noon today.'
'That is impossible, I was on the wreck, miles away.'
'I saw you there, writing it, as distinctly as I see you now,' put in Bruce.
The captain of the wreck turned to the passenger, and said: 'Did you dream that you wrote on a slate?'
'Not that I recall,' replied he.

'Now you speak of dreaming,' said the skipper, 'may I inquire what the gentleman was doing at noon today?'

'Captain,' said the other, 'he had become greatly exhausted, and fell into a heavy sleep, some time before noon, and remained in that condition for over an hour. When he awoke he said to me, "Captain, I am confident that we shall be relieved this very day." When I asked him his reason for so saying, he replied that he had dreamt he was on board a vessel, and that he was convinced she was coming to our rescue. He described her appearance and outward rig and, to our astonishment, when your vessel hove in sight she corresponded exactly to his description. We had not, I must admit, much confidence in his assurance. As it has happened, it looks uncommon like as if Providence had interfered to save us in a very mysterious manner.'

'There can be no doubt about that,' replied the other captain. 'It is due to that writing on the slate, however it came about, that all your lives are saved. I was steering at the time considerably south of west, and I altered my course to nor'west, on account of the writing on the slate.' Then, turning to the passenger, he inquired, 'Did you dream of writing on a slate?'

'Not that I am aware of. I have no recollection of that; but I may say that everything here on board seems to me familiar; yet I am certain that I was never in your vessel before.'

The above account was related to Mr Robert Owen, formerly American minister at Naples, by Captain JS Clarke, of the Julia Hallock, a schooner trading in 1859 between New York and Cuba, who had received it directly from Robert Bruce himself. They sailed together for nearly two years, in 1836 and 1837; so that Captain Clarke had the story from the mate about eight years after the occurrence. Bruce after that became master of the brig Comet, trading to New Brunswick, and she was eventually lost at sea, and Bruce is believed to have perished with her.

# THE SOUND OF FRATRICIDE

Probably the last person one would imagine selected for a supernatural warning was Samuel Foote, a mimic and buffoon. And yet the so-called 'English Aristophanes' not only dwelt in a haunted house, or at least believed so, but was closely connected with the chief characters in one of the most unnatural tragedies our judicial records have preserved.

Foote's maternal uncles were Sir John Gooder and Captain Gooder, a naval officer. In 1740 the two brothers dined at a friend's house near Bristol; for a long time they had been on bad terms owing to certain money transactions, but at the dinner table a reconciliation was, to all appearance, arrived at between them. On his return home, however, Sir John was waylaid by some men from his brother's vessel, acting by his brother's authority, carried on board and deliberately strangled, Captain Gooder not only unconcernedly looking on, but actually furnishing the rope with which the crime was committed. For this atrocity the fratricidal officer and his confederates were tried at the Bristol Assizes, found guilty and executed.

But, say the biographers of Foote, the strangest part of this terrible tale remains to be told. On the night the murder was perpetrated, Foote arrived at his father's house at Truro; he describes himself as having been kept awake for some time by the softest and sweetest strains of music he had ever heard. At first he tried to fancy it was a serenade got up by some of the family to welcome him home; but not being able to discover any trace of the musicians, he was compelled to come to the conclusion that the sounds were the mere offspring of his imagination. Some short time afterwards Foote learnt the particulars of his uncle's terrible fate, and remarking that the murder had been consummated at the same hour of the same night that he had been haunted by the mysterious sounds, he arrived at the conclusion that it was a supernatural warning, and this impression retained to the last moments of his existence.

# THE ANTONY DEATH-BED VISITOR

The following letter was written by Mrs Pole-Carew of Antony House, Torpoint, on 31 December 1883:

In October 1880 Lord and Lady Waldegrave came with their scotch maid, Helen Alexander, to stay with us. (The account then describes how Helen was discovered to have caught typhoid fever.) She did not seem to be very ill in spite of it, and as there seemed no fear of danger, and Lord and Lady Waldegrave had to go a long journey the following day (Thursday), they decided to leave her, as they were advised to do, under their friends' care.

The illness ran its usual course, and she seemed to be going on perfectly well till the Sunday week following, when the doctor told me that the fever had left her, but the state of weakness which had supervened was such as to make him extremely anxious. I immediately engaged a regular nurse, greatly against the wish of Reddell, my maid, who had been her chief nurse all through the illness, and who was quite devoted to her. However, as the nurse could not come till the following day, I allowed Reddell to sit up with her again that night, to give her the medicine and food, which were to be taken constantly.

At about 4.30 that night, or rather Monday morning, Reddell looked at her watch, poured out the medicine, and was bending over the bed to give it to Helen, when the call bell in the passage rang. She said to herself, 'There's that tiresome bell with the wire caught again.' (It seems it did occasionally ring of itself in this manner.) At that moment, however, she heard the door open, and, looking round, saw a very stout old woman walk in. She was dressed in a nightgown and red flannel petticoat, and carried an old-fashioned brass candlestick in her hand. The petticoat had a hole rubbed in it. She walked into the room and appeared to be going towards the dressing table to put her candle down. She was a perfect stranger to Reddell, who, however, merely thought, 'This is her mother come to see after her,' and she felt glad it was so, without reasoning upon it, as one would in a dream. She thought the mother looked annoyed, possibly at not having been sent for before. She then gave Helen the medicine, and turning round, found that the apparition had disappeared, and that the door was shut. A great change, meanwhile, had taken place in Helen, and Reddell fetched me, who sent for the doctor, and meanwhile applied hot poultices, but Helen died a little before the doctor came. She was quite conscious up to about half an hour before she died, when she seemed to be going to sleep.

During the early days of her illness Helen had written to a sister, mentioning her being unwell, but making nothing of it, and as she never mentioned anyone but this sister, it was supposed by the household, to whom she was a perfect stranger, that she had no other relation alive. Reddell was always offering to write for her, but she always declined, saying there was no need, she would write herself in a day or two. No one at home, therefore, knew of her being so ill, and it is, therefore, remarkable that her mother, a far from nervous person, should have said that evening, going up to bed, 'I am sure Helen is very ill.'

Reddell told me and my daughter of the apparition about an hour after Helen's death, prefacing with, 'I am not superstitious, or nervous, and I wasn't the least frightened, but her mother came last night,' and she then told the story, giving a careful description of the figure she had seen. The relations were asked to come to the funeral, and the father, mother and sister came, and in the mother Reddell recognised the apparition, as I did also, for Reddell's description had been most accurate, even to the expression, which she had ascribed to annoyance, but which was due to deafness. It was judged best not to speak about it to the mother, but Reddell told the sister, who said the description of the figure corresponded exactly with the probable appearance of her mother if roused in the night; that they had exactly such a candlestick at home, and that there was a hole in her mother's petticoat produced by the way she always wore it. It seems curious that neither Helen nor her mother appeared to be aware of the visit. Neither of them, at any rate, ever spoke of having seen the other, nor even of having dreamt of having done so.

F.A. Pole-Carew

# THE SEXTON OF CHILTON POLDEN

For some years during the last century, the living of Chilton Polden was held by a clergyman of the name of Drury. The parish was very scattered and interspersed with rough tracts of moorland. One evening in April, while returning home, Mr Drury stumbled on some uneven ground and twisted his ankle very badly. After resting a short time, he tried to pursue his way and, with many pauses and much difficulty, at last reached the Rectory, from which he sent a message asking the doctor to come round at once. The effort of walking the last mile with his injured ankle had had the effect of increasing the swelling and inflammation to such a degree that at the moment the doctor saw it he said, 'There will be no chance, Mr Drury, of your being able to preach for three weeks.'

'That is dreadful news,' answered Mr Drury. 'Why, Easter falls in a fortnight and all the clergy round here have more on their hands than they know how to manage. What shall I do?'
'I really cannot say,' returned the doctor, 'but I do know you will not be able either to officiate or to preach this Easter.'

After the departure of the doctor, Mr Drury thought over the position and at length decided to write to his youngest brother, Frank, who was a curate in Liverpool, to ask if he could come and help him. Very thankful he was too, when in due time a letter arrived from Frank, saying that when his Vicar had read Mr Drury's letter, and understood what had happened, he had been most generous and had given Frank permission to come to Chilton Polden for Palm Sunday and Easter Sunday. Frank ended by promising to turn up in two days' time.

This he did and was delighted to see his brother again, and full of the pleasure of being in the country at so lovely a season, after having spent the winter in the slums of Liverpool. He arrived on the Friday before Palm Sunday.

The next day, when talking to his brother, he said, 'I had a queer dream last night. I thought I was walking around in the churchyard here and that I saw an elderly man, with rather long grey hair and a bent figure, as though he suffered from rheumatism, digging a grave by the south porch of the church. I went up to him and asked whether someone had died lately and for whom he was digging the grave. The man raised himself from his task and looking me full in the face said, quite distinctly, "It is yours, sir." I know it sounds absurd, but the dream gave me a real shock. I had to get up and light a candle and read for an hour before I could sleep again.'

After telling his brother his dream, Frank seemed to forget all about it. In the evening he came in with his hands full of wildflowers, saying, 'I have seen a specimen which I must get tomorrow (Sunday) evening after afternoon service. The plant was growing rather low down under a rock and I had no time today to scramble down to it.'

At morning service on Palm Sunday, Frank chose for his text, 'Lord, remember me when Thou comest into Thy Kingdom.' In the middle of he stopped suddenly and some of the people nearest the pulpit noticed that he had turned rather pale. However, he recovered himself in a moment and went on steadily to the end.

When he got back to the Rectory, he said to Mr Drury, 'Do you know, I have seen the elderly man of my dream in the church this morning. The scare came back to me and for an instant I thought I should not be able to finish my sermon. The man was sitting close to the third pillar on the right hand side of the aisle.' Yes,' replied Mr Drury, 'that is just where old Ben, the sexton, always sits, but your dream, Frank, is nonsense. You are only going to be here another ten days and you are in perfect health. You must just forget your fright and dismiss the whole episode as coincidence.'

Frank was young and cheerful by nature. He either succeeded in forgetting or at any rate appeared to forget. In the afternoon he preached from the text, 'Today shalt thou be with me in Paradise.' When he reached the Rectory he made no further allusion to his dream.

After an early tea together, Frank gaily started off on his expedition to get the flower which he had seen and coveted the day before. When supper time came, he had not returned. Evening faded into dusk and dusk into darkness, and still there was no sign of him. Mr Drury, imprisoned in the house with his swollen ankle, grew uneasy, and at last sent the housekeeper to tell the village constable. A search was at once organised, with lanterns, but that night nothing could be found. In the morning, however, when the search was renewed, Frank's body was discovered at the foot of an old quarry. He held a flower in his hand. He was buried in Chilton Polden churchyard.

## THE LUMINOUS CHAMBER

The following narrative is by Mr T Westwood:

In the year 1840 I was detained for several months in the sleepy old town of Taunton. My chief associate during that time was a fox-hunting squire - a bluff, hearty, genial type of his order with just sufficient intellectuality to temper his animal exuberance. Many were our merry rides through the thorpes and hamlets of pleasant Somersetshire; and it was in one of these excursions, while the evening sky was like molten copper, and a fiery March wind coursed like a racehorse over the open downs, that he related to me the story of what he called his Luminous Chamber.

Coming back from the hunt after dark, he said he had frequently observed a central window in an old hall not far from the roadside, illuminated. All the other windows were dark, but from this one a wan dreary light was visible; and as the owners had deserted the place, and he knew it had no occupant, the lighted window became a puzzle to him.

On one occasion, having a brother squire with him, and both carrying a good store of port wine under their belts, they declared they would solve the mystery of the Luminous Chamber then and there. The lodge was still tenanted by an aged porter; him they roused up, and after some delay, having obtained a lantern and the keys of the hall, they proceeded to make their entry. Before opening the great door, however, my squire averred he had made a careful inspection of the front of the house from the lawn. Sure enough, the central window was illuminated - an eerie, forlorn-looking light made it stand out in contrast to the rest - a dismal light, that seemed to have nothing in common with the world, or the life that is.

The two squires visited all the other rooms, leaving the luminous room till the last. There was nothing noticeable in any of them; they were totally obscure. But on entering the luminous room a marked change was perceptible. The light in it was not full, but sufficiently so to distinguish its various articles of furniture, which were common and scanty enough. What struck them most was the uniform diffusion of the light; it was as strong under the table as on the table, so that no single object projected any shadow on the floor, nor did they themselves project any shadow. Looking into a great mirror over the mantelpiece, nothing could be weirder, the squire declared, than the reflection in it of the dim, wanly-lit chamber, and of the two awe-stricken faces that glared at them from the midst - his own and his companion's. He told me too, that he had not been many seconds in the room before a sick faintness stole over him, a feeling - such was his expression I remember - as if his life were being sucked out of him. His friend owned afterwards to a similar sensation. The upshot of it was that both squires retired crestfallen and made no further attempt at solving the mystery.

It has always been the same, the old porter grumbled; the family had never occupied the room, but really there were no ghosts - the room just had a light of its own. A less sceptical spirit might have opined that the room was full of ghosts - an awful conclave - viewless, inscrutable, but from whom emanated that deathly and deadly luminousness.

## THE DOUBLE AT DINNER

Sir C- T- gave a dinner in honour of two judges of the assize, one of whom enjoyed the hospitalities of his host with all zest and freedom, while the other, unable, as it seemed, to eat or converse, sat wrapped in gloomy abstraction, broken only by such moments of evident uneasiness, that his colleague contrived to bring the banquet to an early termination; soon after which, ordering their horses, the two learned brethren departed in company for the assize-town, D- (Dorchester?).

Scarcely were they alone, when the melancholy judge informed his friend that during the whole period of the repast he had seen the exact double or personification, of Lady T-, their hostess, standing behind that lady's own chair, imitating her every action! That it was no optical delusion, arising from some natural cause, was evidenced by its not applying to any other person or object in the room, and the idea that it might betoken some fatal misfortune to their amiable entertainer, had dwelt so powerfully upon his mind, as to produce the unconquerable depression his friend had noticed.

He was yet speaking when they were overtaken by a servant of the house, who was proceeding at full gallop in search of medical aid, though without much hope that it would prove effectual, the unfortunate lady having, immediately on the departure of the guests, retired to her own apartment and hanged herself.

## A BRISTOL GHOST

The following account was given to psychical researchers by the Rev A Bellamy of Publow, near Bristol.

When a girl at school, my wife made an agreement with a fellow pupil, Miss W-, that the one of them who died first should, if divinely permitted, appear after her decease to her survivor. In 1874 my wife, who had not seen or heard anything of her former school friend for some years, chanced to hear of her death. The news reminded her of her former agreement, and then, becoming nervous, she told me of it. I knew of my wife's compact, but I had never seen a photograph of her friend, or heard any description of her.

A night or two afterwards, as I was sleeping with my wife, a fire brightly burning in the room and a candle alight, I suddenly awoke and saw a lady sitting by the side of the bed where my wife was sleeping soundly. At once I sat up in the bed, and gazed so intently that even now I can recall her form and features. I remember that I was much struck, as I looked intently at her, with the careful arrangement of her coiffure, every single hair being most carefully brushed down. How long I sat and gazed I cannot say, but directly the apparition ceased to be, I got out of bed to see if any of my wife's garments had by any means optically deluded me. I found nothing in the line of vision but a bare wall.

Hallucination on my part I rejected as out of the question, and I doubted not that I had really seen an apparition. Returning to bed, I lay till my wife some hours after awoke and then I gave her an account of her friend's appearance. I described her colour, form, etc, all of which exactly tallied with my wife's recollection of Miss W-. Finally, I asked, 'But was there any special point to strike one in her appearance?' 'Yes,' my wife promptly replied. 'We girls used to tease her at school for devoting

so much time to the arrangement of her hair.' This was the very thing which I have said so much struck me. Such are the simple facts.

# A BRIDGEWATER GHOST

The following account was given to psychical researchers by 'Mrs W-' of E- Vicarage, Somerset.

Some years ago I was driving in a dog-cart with a friend, and just as we were starting to go up the only hill (Wembdon Hill) in this town, the mare slowed down and stopped four times. I flicked the whip, and laughingly said, 'It is a case of Balaam and his ass again,' and the words were hardly out of my mouth, when the strangest apparition glided down a steep path, crossed the road and disappeared through a gate on the left. It was a very cold October day, about 11.30 am, and she was wearing a high-waisted muslin dress, and a white silk shawl over her head, and as she passed through the gate she seemed to stare straight at me with a horrible look on her face. The mare reared till she had passed over the road, and then galloped up the steep hill and it was not until we had gone two miles that I could pull her up. We both saw the apparition and my friend fainted, and altogether it was a mercy we were not all killed! Naturally, I could not make any inquiries without making a scare, but I did learn later on that when a house was being built about eighty years ago, the skeleton of a man was found, and I was told that he had been murdered by his wife, but although I have passed the same place many times, I have never been able to see her again.

# THE GHOST OF THE CORRIDOR

For several years past, singular rumours have got abroad, from time to time, relative to an old family seat near F-, Somersetshire, which, however, despite its reputation, has never up to the present moment been without occupants. The circumstance most frequently associated with the rumours aforesaid, was that, on almost every night, at twelve o'clock, something that was invisible entered a certain corridor at one end, and passed out at the other. It mattered not to the mysterious intruder who might be witnesses of the midnight progress. Almost as regularly as night succeeded day, the strange sound recurred, and was precisely that which would have been occasioned by a lady, wearing the high-heeled shoes of a former period, and a full silk dress, sweeping through the corridor. Nothing was ever seen, and the impression produced by hearing the approach, the passing, and withdrawal of the visitor with perfect distinctness, while the companion sense (of sight) was shut, was described as most extraordinary.

It was but a day or two since, that the brother of the writer chanced to meet at dinner one of the more recent ear-witnesses of this certainly most remarkable phenomenon, and the adventure shall be given nearly in his own words:

'I was visiting, about two years ago, at a friend's house a few miles from F-, when my attention was attracted, one day at dinner, to a conversation that was going on, having reference to the haunted character of B- House near F-. The subject seemed to interest the speakers so much that I begged to be informed of the details, and learned that a particular corridor of the mansion in question was, every night, at twelve o'clock, the scene of an occurrence that had hitherto defied all explanation. One of the party had himself been a visitor at B- House, and, being sceptical and devoid of fear, requested permission to keep vigil in the haunted gallery. He did so, witnessed the phenomenon, and 'nothing on earth' he frankly owned, 'would induce me to repeat the experiment.' He then recounted to me certain circumstances, which agreed so nearly with what I myself subsequently witnessed, that it will be better to relate them from the direct evidence of my own astonished senses.

My curiousity being greatly increased by the manifest belief accorded by those present to this gentleman's story, I obtained an introduction to the family of B- House, and received from them ready permission to pass a night, or more if necessary, in the haunted corridor. I was at full liberty, moreover, to choose any companion I wished for the adventure, and I accordingly invited an old friend, Mr W-K, who happened to be shooting in the neighbourhood, to accompany me.

W-K, like myself, was disposed to incredulity in such matters; he had never seen anything of the sort before, and was positively assured either that nothing unusual would occur on the night when two such sentries were on duty, or that we should have no great difficulty tracing the phenomenon to a fleshly source.

The family at B- House happened at this period to be from home, but authority having been given us to make any arrangements we pleased, W-K and I proceeded to the mansion, intending, at all events, to devote two nights to the experiment. It will be seen that this part of the plan was not strictly carried out!

We dined early, at five o'clock, and in order to make certain of the clearness of our heads, drank nothing but a little table beer. We had then six hours before us but resolved to lose no chance, we took up position at once in the haunted corridor. It was of considerable length, with a door at each extremity, and one or two at the side. My friend W-K is a good picquet player, and as our watch was to be a prolonged one, and it was extremely desirable to keep ourselves well on the alert, it was agreed to take some cards with us.

Combining business with pleasure, we placed our card-table so as completely to barricade the passage; our two chairs exactly filling up the space that remained, so that it would be impossible for any mortal creature to press through without disturbing us. In addition to this we placed two lighted candles on the floor near the wall, at two or three feet from the table, on the side from which the mysterious footsteps always came. Finally, we placed two revolvers and two life-preservers on the table.

These precautions taken, we commenced our game and played with varying success till about eleven o'clock; at that time, growing a little tired of picquet, we changed the game to écarté, and played until the house clock sounded midnight. Mechanically we dropped our cards, and looked along the dim corridor. No sounds, however, followed, and after pausing a minute or two, we resumed the game, which chanced to be near its conclusion.

'I say, it's nonsense sitting up,' yawned W-K, 'this thing never comes, you know, after twelve. What do you say? After this game?'

I looked at my watch, which I had taken the precaution to set by the church clock as we entered the village. By this it appeared that the house clock was fast. It wanted yet three minutes of the hour. Pointing out the mistake to W-K, I proposed that we should wait another ten minutes.

The words were not fairly out of my mouth, when the door at the end seemed to open and reclose. This time the cards literally dropped from our hands, for, though nothing could be seen, the conviction was growing on both our minds that something had entered. We were soon more fully convinced of it. The silence was broken by a tapping sound, such as would be caused by a light person wearing high-heeled shoes, quietly coming towards us up the gallery, each step, as it approached, sounding more distinct than the last exactly, in fact, as would be the case under ordinary circumstances. It was a firm and regular tread - light but determined - and it was accompanied by a sound between a sweep, a rustle and a whistle, not comparable to anything but the brushing of a stiff, silken dress against the walls.

How W-K and I looked as the sounds advanced as it were to storm us, I will not pretend to say. I confess I was, for the moment, petrified with amazement, and neither of us, I believe, moved hand or foot. On - on - on came the tap and rustle; they reached the lighted candles on the floor, passed them, not even disturbing the flame, then the tapping ceased, but the invisible silken robe seemed to brush the wall on both sides, on a level with our heads, then the tapping recommenced on the other side of the table, and so, receding, made its exit at the other door!

As for making any use of our revolvers or life-preservers, the idea never once occurred to either of us. There was not even a shadow at which to strike; it was sound alone.

I feel that any attempt to explain this strange phenomenon at once to my own satisfaction and that of others, would be perfectly futile. I must of necessity simply content myself with narrating the fact as it had occurred, and as it had been, and probably may yet be, witnessed by many others, as little predispose as my friend W-K and I to be made the dupe of any human artifice. I may mention that, on one occasion, it chanced that a nurse in the family had to pass through the corridor about the hour of twelve, carrying or rather leading a little girl who was deaf and dumb. As the sounds passed, the child appeared to shrink back in the utmost alarm, struggling and moaning to get away, nor could she ever be induced to enter the corridor again without evincing the same violent terror.

## A GHOSTLY PROPHET

The following account appears in *Strange Things Among Us*, by Henry Spicer, published in 1863. The lady who wrote it 'belongs to an old and distinguished family - a name, were it permissible to mention it, probably familiar to most of the readers of this work'.

On the fourteenth of May 18-, I was at W- near Weymouth. The house is an old one, and has peculiarities of construction, some of which, in order to make my story clear, I must endeavour to explain.

The great drawing room upstairs is a singularly shaped apartment, having the door in one corner, and opposite to a large window opening on the balcony.

On the left-hand side of the door is one opening into a very small room, so small as almost to be termed a closet, having a window divided in the centre by a stone mullion, and a small place where there had at one time stood an altar, with a recess for holy water, proving that the little chamber had been formerly used as an oratory. The window looks down, at a great elevation, upon a flagged courtyard, and is over what was, in former days, the chapel, now used as a pantry. From this oratory there are no means of exit, save through the drawing room.

The door of the drawing room opens onto a small landing having the old winding stone staircase on the right; and facing the door, is a wide corridor, on to which open all the bedrooms. My daughter-in-law, being rather an invalid, had been reclining all day on the sofa in the drawing room.

Towards dusk, I was in the bedroom with the children, and, leaving it to prepare for tea, met my daughter-in-law coming from the drawing room. Standing on the landing, she asked me the way to the morning room, and I had just pointed down the winding stairs, when I caught sight of a man, tall and with grey hair, passing across the drawing room, from the fire towards the wall by the oratory. He passed between me and the lamp, which stood on the table near the window, and brightly lit up the whole room.

I enquired who was the stranger that had been with her in the drawing-room. My daughter-in-law, with some surprise, denied that any one had come in and presently left me. Conceiving, however, that she must have been mistaken, I remained where I was, every moment expecting that the man, whoever he might be, would come out, and, when I found he did not do so, wondering whither he could have be taken himself, since he appeared to me to walk straight up to the wall, and (though the oratory door remained closed) there disappear. My first idea was that he was a robber, who proposed to conceal himself somewhere about the rooms, and I consequently determined to watch him.

Observing no place of concealment in the drawing-room, I went at once to the oratory, and, cautiously unclosing the door, looked in, half expecting to be grasped by the discovered marauder. No one was there! Having searched every corner and ascertained that no human being could have escaped by the window, I returned to the drawing-room, and, going out on the landing, still watching the door, I called to one of the young ladies of the house, and asked her laughingly whether she had ever seen a ghost in the house.

'Never,' was her reply, 'but you know that there is one?'
I had never heard so, but I now declared that I had certainly seen it, and that not many minutes since.
My friend laughed, and said, 'You don't mean to say that you have seen the old man?'
'What old man?'
'Our ghost!'

I described his appearance, and the manner in which he had so strangely vanished. Miss M- appeared much struck, and proposed a closer search, whereupon we lit our candles, and examined systematically every corner of the drawing-room, the oratory and the balcony, but without success.

I am not what is called a believer in ghosts. I never before saw anything I could not account for, nor can I perceive any use or purpose in what I saw that evening. I only know I did see it, and that, standing in a dusky corridor, and looking straight into a well-lighted room, I cannot conceive that I was the subject of an optical illusion.

As the face of the figure was averted, I cannot give a more minute description of it, but the apparition was so natural and palpable, that the last thing that occurred to me was that it might be 'a dream of the feverish brain.'

We had just concluded our scrutiny, when the gentlemen, who had been smoking on the lawn, came upstairs, and were informed of what had occurred. One of the party immediately declared that it was the ghost of W-. On my pressing for further explanation, they related that most extraordinary story, given, as I have been told, in an early edition of Hutchins' *History of Dorset.* This exceedingly rare book, the greater part of the impression having been destroyed by fire at the publisher's in 1660, was in the possession of Mr Rickard. This gentleman was lying on what was expected to be his deathbed, when, one day, he begged his wife, who sat at his bedside, to leave him alone for a few minutes with the reverend rector of the parish, Mr Bound, who was likewise in the room.

As soon as she had quitted them, Mr Rickard directed his friend's attention towards the foot of the bed, asking at the same time in a mysterious tone:

'Do you hear what the old man is saying?'

Unable to comprehend him, Mr Bound looked with amazement at the speaker, when the latter calmly requested him to bring pen, ink and paper, and commit to writing what he was about to hear.

The reverend minister obeyed, when Mr Rickard, with the manner of one following the dictation of another sitting at the foot of the bed, pronounced the following prophecy:
'In the year 1665, more than ninety thousand persons will perish in London of one disease.' (The Plague).
'In the succeeding year of 1666, there will occur such a fire in London that the lead on the roof of St Paul's will pour down like rain.' (The Great Fire of London).
'On the 11th of June, 1685, a person will land west of Weymouth, who shall be the cause of great calamity and blood shed, and involve many leading families of the west in trouble and ruin.' (Monmouth Rebellion).
'In 1688, events will come to pass that shall entirely change the constitution of this land.' (Bill of Rights).
'And that you may know that what I tell you is true, though you are today supposed to be in a dying state, and unable to leave your bed, you will tomorrow be well enough to rise, and walk out upon your terrace. While there, you will receive three unlooked for visits, one from a gentleman from Ireland, one from a

person from Jersey, and one from your son, whom you believe to be far distant abroad, and whom you had not hoped again to see.'

Thus ran this extraordinary communication and accordingly, on the following morning, the invalid really found himself so much better that he was able to walk upon his terrace. While doing so, an old friend arrived, who had just come across from Ireland; another visitor appeared, who had just landed at Weymouth from a Jersey vessel; and finally young Rickard, the unexpected son, drove hastily to the door.

This wonderful statement was signed by Mr Rickard, and the reverend Mr Bound, and verified before two magistrates of the county, one of whom was Mr J Stranwayes, an ancestor of the Earl of Ilchester. The name of the other I cannot recollect.

Readers may like to compare the version in Hutchins' *History of Dorset*, given below. Curiously the story does not appear in the early and rare editions, but only in the third edition published in 1861, two years before the publication in which the previous description appeared, so it would have been easily accessible at that time. The name of the visionary has changed, and it is clear he is suffering from a mental disorder. The dates 1665, 1666 and 1685 and the death toll of the Plague have been helpfully inserted into the prophesy.

## A PROPHESY

Related by Mr John Sadler, late of Warmwell in the County of Dorset, who was a very learned and pious man, in the yeare after the return of King Charles the Second (i.e.1661).

The said Mr Sadler, being under some distemper of minde, kept his chamber, and had his servant, one Thomas Gray, of the same parish, to attend him there and I, Cuthbert Bownd, minister of the parish, comeing to visit him where I found

him setting up in his bed, his wife and servant being with him. He caused his wife presently to departe, and the door to be shut, and made his man to come on the one side of the bed and myselfe on the other, and looking very earnestly towards the end of the roome, asked us whether we saw noe body, nor heard noe voice, and we answered him that we neither saw nor heard anything, but perswaded him to lie downe in his bed and to take some rest, and he bad us be quiet, for there was a man that had great things to tell him, and spake so loude that he did wonder that we did not heare him; and presently ordered his man to fetch pen, inck and paper, and lookeing towards the place where the man stood, he began to write, and soe wrote on as if the old man did still dictate to him, and every now and then would be askeing him whether it was soe or not, and after he had ended the matter he read the pages distinctly over twice, and at the end asked whether he had written right. He then caused us to sett our hands to the paper, 'for he will not be gone until he sees that done.' When we had done it, he said, 'Now he is gone,' meaning the old man he had told us of.

What he related to us:
That there would die in the city of London soe many thousands, mentioning the number, which I have forgotten, and the time that the city would be burnt downe, great parte of it, and that he saw Poles (St Paul's) tumbled downe, as if beaten downe with great guns.

That we should have three sea-fights with the Dutch; and that there would appear three blazing stars, and that the last should be terrible to behold.

That afterwards there should come three small ships to land in the west of Weymouth, that would put all England in an uproar, but it would come to nothing.

That in the year 1688 there would come to pass such a thing in this kingdome that all the world would take notice of it. That after all this, there would come good times, and that I should live to see great things come to pass, but he and his man should die; and further that some wonderfull thing should come to pass afterwards, which he was not to make known.

That he should be able to goe abroad the next day and there would come three men to see him, one from Ireland and one from Jersey, and his brother Bingham, which did certainly come as he had told us and I saw him walking early in the morning the next day in his ground. Upon the report of this, his man Thomas Gray and myselfe were sent for before the deputy lieutenants of the county, and made affidavit of the truth of this before Colonel Giles Stranwaies, Colonel Coker, and many others yet alive, within three or four days after he told it me.

# THE GHOST OF THE DANCING TREE

There were on either side of the Tamar in olden times a number of large ancient trees which had been so pollarded that it was customary to hold dances among their upper boughs. In Devon there were such trees at Moretonhampstead, Lifton, Great Fulford and Meavy, and in Cornwall there is at Trebursye near Launceston an ancient oak, now (1900) in a neglected condition having lost most of its original form and looking merely a peculiarly crabbed and tortured old tree.

Here anciently a ghost was wont to be seen, that of a woman who had fallen from it during a dance and broken her neck, and many stories were afloat relative to horses taking fright at night and running away with the riders, or of passers-by on foot who were so scared as to be unable to continue their journey, through seeing the dead woman dancing on the tree. At length matters became so serious that Parson Ruddle, vicar of Launceston, a notable man in his way and famous as a ghost-layer, was induced to go to the tree at nightfall and exorcise the unquiet spirit. The ghost had so effectually frightened people that the dances on the top of the tree were discontinued and never resumed.

# THE GHOSTLY MOTHER

A brother of Sir Philip Egerton took up a living in Devonshire, and went to take possession of it. He had not been long in his rectory before, coming one day into his study, he found an old lady there, seated in an armchair by the fire. Knowing no old lady could really be there, and thinking the appearance must be the result of indigestion, he summoned all his courage and boldly sat down upon the old lady, who disappeared. The next day he met the old lady in the passage, rushed up against her, and she vanished. But he met her a third time, and then, feeling it could not always have been indigestion, he wrote to his sister in Cheshire, begging her to call upon the Misses Athelstan, sisters of the clergyman who had previously held the living, and to say what he had seen. When they heard it, the Misses Athelstan looked inexpressibly distressed and said, 'That was our mother; we hoped it was only to us she would appear. When we were there she appeared constantly, but when we left we hoped she would be at rest.'

# THE GHOST OF DOWRICH

Dowrich is an estate in Sandford, near Crediton. Half a mile from the house is a stream crossed by a low bridge. The last of the Dowrishes, returning home from a considerable consumption of punch at the home of a hospitable neighbour, fell from his horse here on a cold winter's night, and was killed.

His ghost has from that time been gradually mounting the hill towards the house, at the painfully slow rate of a cock-stride every full moon. But he may not use the road. A bridge is provided for the unfortunate squire, a bridge as narrow and as sharp as the edge of a sword, unrolling itself as he advances. Whenever he falls off, which is often, he is obliged to return to the stream where his life was ended and to begin again. His present position is therefore uncertain, but there is no doubt that one day he will reach the front door, and there is no way of knowing what may happen then.

## TREGAGLE'S HOUSE

John Tregagle of Trevorder, in St Breock parish, was an estate manager who cheated several families out of property during the Civil War period, and found his way into Cornish folklore as 'Jan Tregeagle', a demonic condemned soul.

The old manor house in which that wild and wicked spirit dwelt in life is now a farm. One autumn afternoon the farmer had occasion to go down to Wadebridge just as dusk was falling. His wife accompanied him and they left no one in the house. It was dark when they returned, and they had no sooner set foot in the farmyard than they saw the house was lighted up in all its windows. The shutters were unclosed. Strange forms in antique dresses were passing to and fro. A long table was set with bottles and decanters such as the farmer never saw, and the most unholy noise was issuing from the room. Shouts, oaths, scraps of obscene song, bursts of wild laughter, appalled the two simple people who stood barred out from their home. At last the farmer plucked up courage and marched up to the door. He had no sooner put the key in the lock than every light went out. The howls and cries dropped instantly into silence. The sudden absolute stillness was as awful as the noise. The farmer and his wife went from room to room, but all were empty, and of the riotous carousal there was no trace.

Under a night-sky the church is scarcely visible. But if the clouds roll back from the moon, and let a sudden blaze of light fall over the riverbed, you will see the old grey tower clearly, standing out from a group of chestnut trees, and may even discern an open space beside the churchyard wall, where the high road meets the lane leading to the village. The road gleams beneath the moonlight, but you are too far distant to see any object moving on it.

If it were otherwise, you might see - but never save when the moon is bright - a white rabbit gambolling beside the churchyard wall, a pretty, long-eared rabbit like a child's pet escaped from its hutch. It goes loppeting about among the grasses by the corner of the marsh, and if anyone should pass, will look at him with fearless eyes. And well it may. No villager would attempt to catch it. No boy would aim a blow at it. If anyone walking late sees the white rabbit lopping at his heels, he makes no attempt to drive it away, but quickens his pace, and hopes. A belated postman, terrified at finding he could not shake off the pretty white creature, lost his head and struck fiercely at it with his cudgel. He felt the stick fall on the soft back of the rabbit, such a blow as might have killed a much larger animal. But the rabbit lopped on as if nothing had happened. The cudgel it was which was broken - shivered into splinters as though it had struck a rock.

It was in our great-grandparents' time that the last deliberate effort to meddle with the rabbit took place. The attempt was made by a stranger. A number of young men were drinking in a bar-room at the chief inn of Wadebridge and, as the evening wore on, the talk grew heated. Then somebody spoke of the white rabbit. Instantly the stranger began to jeer - a silly story such as that would never be believed outside a poky little country town where nobody had anything better to do than listen to such tales. What harm could a rabbit do anybody? He would like nothing better than to shoot it.

One of the others drew aside the shutter and looked out. The street was as bright as day, and overhead they could see the new moon sailing, free of clouds. 'Tha'd best go now,' he said. 'When the moon shines like this, tha'll find the rabbit by the church.'

A gun was hanging on the wall. It was taken down and loaded amid a babble of jeers and angry retorts; and then the party crowded to the door to watch the stranger stride down the moonlit street, whistling merrily as he went. They saw him pass onto the bridge, and then went back to their bottles.

But some strange feeling of uneasiness had settled over them. Not one seemed inclined to sit down again. They moved restlessly about the room and presently one of them went to the door and looked out. The others asked eagerly if he heard anything, though they knew the stranger could not have reached the church. Then one suggested it was a shame to allow a man who had no knowledge of his danger to encounter it alone. The others agreed, and without more delay set off in a body. They trudged along saying nothing. When they came near the church they heard a report and a loud cry. With one accord they ran for ward with beating hearts. Neither man nor rabbit was to be seen. They ran up and down calling his name, but there was no reply. He was not in the lane, nor on the road. At last, one of them leapt onto the churchyard wall, and sprang down on the inner side, calling on his friends to follow him. There they found him lying dead, one barrel of the gun discharged, and the contents buried in his body.

That happened many years ago, but still the stranger may be seen leaning over the low wall, pointing an ancient flint-lock gun at some object which moves quickly in the long grass.